Without Seeming to Care at All

Without Seeming to Care at All

Professional Bartenders

Nearly everyone who works in the bar is trying to make it as an artist or something. We are trying to make it as dancers, writers, shoemakers and DJs, actors, tattooists, costume designers and developers. The head of security runs a record label and Little Luke just got back from running on a film set in LA.

We do not care about the bar and yet we find we cannot help but care a little. *Do not care,* we say, as we pick at a sticky piece of gum on the table. *Do not care,* as we stack menus neatly beside the cask pumps. But often it is so busy there is no time to talk to ourselves, there is no time to remember that we do not care.

Sometimes people ask us what else we do. They want to know what we are trying to make it as. Is it not enough to work in a bar, we think? Why do we have to be trying to make it? It is exhausting being two people all the time. Nothing else, we say, just a professional bartender. We want it both ways.

Regeneration

On this sliver of island between the A road and the canal we will not last much longer. We will keep on until we get thrown out of our warehouses because it is still cheaper and better than anywhere else. We cannot sleep for the sound of cranes and drills. In the grey dawn, construction workers in high visibility jackets watch us stagger home.

Squee

A certain woman is entitled to free drinks. She has a black cat called Squee who goes everywhere with her. He curls up on her lap while she drinks her free drinks and flirts with the boys behind the bar.

She says she has lived on the island for longer than any of us. When she arrived with Squee all the warehouses round here were squats and there were no bars, breweries or coffee shops. We did what we wanted, she says. It was real rock 'n' roll.

Then people started paying to live in the warehouses and other people opened bars, breweries and coffee shops and people came from elsewhere to eat and drink and it was all because they wanted to be close to the real rock 'n' roll.

After a few drinks she says, people like you are just here because of people like me. Squee cannot bear it when she is drunk and goes out the front to stare at the birds on the canal.

She wants us to think she gets her free drinks because she is the mother of the island. But really it is because of Squee. Every night we lock him in the bar and every morning he leaves a neat pile of dead mice. It is cheaper than paying for pest control.

Fast Food

The owners call the head chef into their office and ask her if it is true that X is taking speed at work. The head chef says it is true but adds that she does not consider X a problem. The real problem for me is Y, she says. What is Y doing? ask the owners. Well he's the only one not taking speed, says the head chef, and he's just not fast enough.

Summer and Winter

In the summer everyone comes to the island, the bars around the car park are always full and every day is a fiesta. There are more shifts available and we have more money. The shifts are harder and longer but when they are done we are flush with adrenaline and cash. Every conversation seems full of possibility: what drugs can we get? what DJs are on? who's sleeping with who? Our friends from elsewhere come to the island and we all go out together, drinking and snorting, gibbering and dancing until the window panes turn white with sun. After, we stagger back to someone's room to take downers and fall asleep on their sofa.

In the winter, no one comes to the island, the bars are empty and the days drag. There are fewer shifts and less cash. We cannot afford the drugs or the tickets to see the DJs. We do not ask who is sleeping with who because we know the answer. We are each other's only company and we are bored by the sound of our voices.

Once in a while someone will say, enough is enough. They will call friends from elsewhere, friends they have not seen in a long time, perhaps the same friends who came to the island in the summer. They will call them and arrange to go for a drink. Any place except the island, they will say. Then they will go off to the centre or even the other end of the city. But they always wash back in on the last train to find us drinking in the bar. We make them stand there for a bit, holding their hat in their hands like an apology, before we make room for them on the sofa.

The One Where They Fired the Head Chef

The owners said the head chef had snorted coke off the bar. It was winter, discipline was fraying and they wanted to make a point. She said, no she had not snorted coke off the bar. If any coke had been snorted at all, and she was not saying there had been, it would have been racked up on her phone in the toilet. They played her the CCTV footage. Look, she pointed, everyone is going to the toilet! Wait, the owners said. She watched herself come out of the toilet and pick at the tiny speaker hole on her phone for some time. Then she put her phone on the bar, took a rolled up note from her bra and bent over the phone. See, the owners said. She threw up her hands. For fuck's sake, there was just a bit stuck! It was so unfair, she thought, the owners were always snorting coke off the bar.

Pressure Vessel

We have so many images, smells and sounds inside us. Athens. Familiar brown smoke haze over Piraeus. São Paulo. A three-legged cat on a side street in Pisa. Rubber and tarmac steaming. Marseille. Madagascar. Melbourne. Sand in our swimsuits. Jungle on the car stereo jumping lights to catch the waves south of Durban. How do we fit all that between the A road and the canal?

Sharp sound of stilettos on cobblestones. Durham. Edinburgh. Screech of a tram car in Copenhagen. Croydon. Catholic clamour of a family meal table. Sun in San Francisco. Sheets of rain in County Mayo. Grass thick and wet as a sponge. How do we fit all that into this car park with its four bars, two breweries and one coffee shop?

Un-ironic anarchic graffiti in Prague, Poznan. Sunrise on the third day of not sleeping through the windows of Berghain, Barcelona, some rave outside Bristol. Red steel girders in Tirana. Sight of our own breath under street lights in Stockholm, Toronto. Pigeon pecking at gravel outside a cinema in Warsaw, Whakatane, Wakefield. How do we fit all that into this car park with its potholes full of rain?

If we took out all the images, smells and sounds inside us, unwrapped them and laid them flat on the ground, it would be too much for this sliver of island. Perhaps that is why we do not sleep. We are like fifty litres of beer in a pressure vessel. Between us we have pressed so much of the world into such a small space.

Real Houses

A few of us live in real houses with internal walls and housemates who work day jobs. Sometimes we go back to these houses to wind down. We settle into the front room, hook our phones up to the speakers, crack open cans, improvise ash trays and rack up lines on a DVD case. Around sunrise the housemates start appearing in the kitchen, wearing suits or cycling gear. We introduce ourselves cheerfully but they pour themselves a bowl of cereal and eat it in silence, radiating resentment.

The Sirens

There have always been the young ones and the old ones. Some of us are so young we are not even twenty and others are past forty.

The young ones encourage the old ones. Come on you grannies! they say, offering lines to everyone. Come on you old hoovers, get this down you. The old ones are flattered to be included but in the mornings the young ones chatter about their hangovers brightly and unconvincingly while the old ones can hardly speak.

The old ones encourage the young ones too. When they doubt their choices: all these drugs, this bar work, trying to make it. Keep doing it until you stop enjoying it, the old ones say. If you're still enjoying it, keep doing it. They want the young ones to be just like them. It is not that they are trying to lure the young ones into danger or make them crash upon the rocks. They will do all that to themselves.

Without Seeming to Care at All

He arrives at the bar between nine and ten and spends an hour making tea and regaling us with stories from the night before. His outfits are always extraordinary. For example: brown corduroy trousers, fur coat, trapper hat with flaps unbuttoned. Or: Soviet-era boiler suit, jackboots. He is covered in old world tattoos, pictures of ships and skeletons, quotes in Gothic font, the largest across his chest which reads: Sorrow Found Me When I Was Young.

Sometimes he grades us on our attempts at style. He went to fashion school and has certain rules. Never wear blue with black. Only wear sandals if you are going to wear socks full of pizzazz. Do everything without seeming to care at all.

When he makes it to the office he spends another hour going through emails. He is not interested in work emails, only spam. He keeps a sprawling word document where he copies and pastes his favourite non sequiturs.

For example: *Hey bar, want to quickly become a better screw? As arrogant as this sounds, I live full-time. Flannel corked, if you can afford it. BEST RAMEN I HAVE EVER HAD. So my daughter and I had a date night last night. Effectually probably better than my wife.* He says it is more honest than writing fiction.

At some point he works. He prepares for it by groaning, describing his hangover and burping loudly in the small office. He complains about the owners, his chair, his bad back, his gout. When he has exercised his voice enough he starts calling our suppliers. While on the phone, his tone changes and he seems happy even. But as soon as he hangs up, he calls them a load of fucking morons, space cadets in need of a shag, shitfucks.

When he breaks for lunch he is exhausted as if he has already worked a hard shift. He has pizza every day, with extra cheese. He eats with abandon: tomato on his chin, mouth wide open, shouting about the poor quality of the mozzarella. He used to work at a dairy yard. It was there he slipped a disc in his back. When he comes round our houses, he takes the cheese from our fridge and eats it straight out the pack like a chocolate bar.

In the afternoon he plays solitaire and searches online for log cabins. It is his dream to live in the middle of nowhere. He moved to London in 1997 to go to fashion school but it did not suit him and when everyone else was trying to make it in the industry, he checked out. He has been working in bars since.

If he is happy he draws. He has a notebook filled with intricate sketches. The backdrops are dark and uncomfortably close: tangles of thick trees, the leaning walls of a suburban front room, dystopian wastelands, storm clouds. The figures are startling and obscene: swollen penises, distended vaginas, skeleton accordion players. In one, a tree with a disfigured scrotum, in another, a head vomits up a medley of demonic imps. The only innocents in these carnivals of violence are animals: horses with flaring nostrils, mangy dogs.

If he likes one he rips the page out and takes it home to turn into a full scale etching. He does nothing with these prints. He has no intention of putting together a portfolio, getting an agent or trying to sell his work. He draws for the sake of it. He berates us all for trying to make it. He tells us that selling out means starting to believe in things. It means believing in approval, in success, in money, in yourself. All that bullshit, he says.

At five o'clock he comes to the bar and orders a drink. If the owners are standing nearby he will add loudly, and I'm not paying for that. He does this to make a point. He is the only one of us who remembers the old days of the bar when there was no distinction between owners and managers, when everyone drank with and trusted each other, when the owners did not talk about Gross Profit Margins and Brand Identity, when the drinks were free. He does not say all this. He simply does not pay.

He drinks at the bar all evening and we go to him with our problems. We tell him about the friend who is drifting away, the parent who is ill, the relationship beginning to splinter. He is good at listening, hunched on the bar stool, cradling his pint, his head tilted. When we are done, he slides his drink across. Fuck it, he says, drink this. He encourages us to care less. Then he distracts us with some story to make us laugh.

Later when he is drunk, he changes the music to Wu-Tang Clan and turns it right up. Later still, he dims the lights until the customers can hardly see their food and plays jungle so loud the speakers pop. He stands on a bar stool and counts the beats with his hand in the air. He makes us smile and we dance as we work. We would never do this ourselves. If the owners came in they would be furious. But he does not care what the owners think of him or what happens to him and we are safe under the wing of his nihilism.

When we have closed the bar he sits in the middle of the sofa and we coalesce around him. He is obnoxious, coarse, unpredictable, funny. Once we had a leaving party for a boy who was quitting to freelance as a website developer. He spent the whole night berating the boy for selling out. When the boy fell asleep he unzipped his trousers and rubbed his cock over the boy's face. He filmed himself doing it on his phone and sent it to the developer the next day with the message— something to remember us by.

When he decides to leave he pushes himself to his feet and staggers out without saying goodbye. We are sad to see him go though perhaps a little relieved.

The Many Ways People Might End Up in a Canal

There are many ways people might end up in a canal. Once there was a fight which finished with one man throwing the other in. Another time two boys were playing frisbee and one tripped and fell in. After the first football match at the new stadium nearby, one of the fans climbed onto the bridge and jumped in—but the water is only four foot deep so he was taken away in an ambulance. We saw a girl drop her iPhone in, then climb in after. And one night a woman just walked in—it was dark and she thought the algae was solid ground.

One Way to Come Out of a Canal

The police pulled a body out of the canal this morning. They laid it on the bank opposite the bar, wrapped in white plastic. It is nearly dark and the body is still there. Policemen in bright yellow jackets have been getting in and out of their cars all day. We are on the border between two boroughs and the councils are still arguing over who is responsible for the body.

Do You Know What I Mean?

One Friday B turned up to work nearly in tears. He worked on security and was the biggest, toughest man we ever met. Once we saw him carry someone out the bar, lay him on the floor of the car park and sit on him. He sat there and smoked a cigarette until the police came. He was also one of the most thoughtful people we worked with. At the start of every shift B would go to each of the four bars round the car park and shake hands with every person who was working, remembering their name and asking how they were doing. He even remembered things we told him from the week before.

This Friday he kept taking off his sunglasses to wipe his eyes before putting them on again even though it was cloudy. It was his brother, he said when we asked him. He had been stabbed and was in hospital.

It turned out that B, his brother and a couple of other families ran the drugs in the area where he lived. A woman had ordered some coke. When B's brother turned up to her block, she buzzed him in. On the stairwell he was set upon by three guys who stabbed him several times in the stomach and took the coke. He had somehow managed to get back to his car and drive home.

Now I don't know what to do, B said. My mum says, leave it B, leave it. Because she doesn't want me to go back to prison, see. But that lady set my brother up. She knew they was waiting for him and we can't be having people pull shit like that. I know she's a lady but we have to send a message, do you know what I mean?

We nodded. We said we knew what he meant even though we did not. Or rather, we only knew the way we knew about the world of a gangster film. We did not really know. But we said we knew because at the time it seemed as if that was what he was asking us to say.

Politics

It is not cool to talk about politics; or rather it is pretentious to talk about politics; or it is pretentious to think that we know enough about politics to be able to talk about it when we are too cynical to believe what we read; or rather, because we are too cynical to believe what we read we do not read so it is more accurate to say we are too cynical to believe what we would have read had we been naive enough to read it; or perhaps we do not talk about politics because we read nothing and so know nothing about politics; or because we are afraid to be seen to know nothing about politics because it is not cool to be stupid. In any case, we do not talk about it.

The Accountant and the Drug Dealer

No one knew why the accountant confronted the drug dealer. Not only was he small and quiet but he wore glasses and stammered when he spoke. Most days when he finished work he hurried straight to the bus stop, but on this particular afternoon he was drinking tea in the car park when a black Volkswagen pulled up. The drug dealer slid down his window and asked the accountant if he wanted any cocaine and when the accountant did not reply he held out a business card which read, *Aim Higher* and a telephone number. He was new to the area and wanted to be known. The accountant took the card and returned his hand to his coat pocket. Then he leant down, so he was level with the open car window, and said quite clearly that he was going to hand this card over to the police. The drug dealer looked incredulous, then angry. He leapt out of the car and punched the accountant hard in the temple, before driving off. The accountant went into a state of shock and had to be taken home by the operations officer who, like everyone else in the bar, could not understand why such a small and quiet man had done this.

The Saplings

It took the handyman two full days to plant the saplings. He built six wooden troughs along the edge of the canal and filled them with soil and wood shavings. Then he planted the trees and clipped cylinders of plastic netting around them for protection, like he had seen in parks.

When it was done he drank his beer at the canal side tables, gazing at the saplings and smiling. As we passed him to run food, he said, they're fucking beautiful eh? And we had to agree with him.

He was a strong man with a loud laugh and grey hair that fell in waves over his neck. But there was something dangerous about him too. He had long scars on his arms and when we asked him about them he said he had done some naughty things Down Under and fell silent.

The following Saturday he came to the bar to drink. It was summer. The outside area along the canal was jammed with people and the railings along the side of the building were full with bikes. They were so full that a boy brought his fixie round to the canal side area, hoisted it into one of the troughs and leant it against a sapling.

Within seconds the handyman was at his side. You can't lean your bike there mate. Who are you? said the boy. Never mind who the fuck I am, the handyman said, you can't lean it on that sapling. He was halfway through his fifth beer and rocked on his feet as he spoke. The boy snorted, mate, I'll leave it where I want, and turned away.

The handyman placed his pint carefully on the next table and came back to the boy. He seized him under both armpits and hauled him into the air as easily as you might lift a baby. Listen mate, he said. It's either you, or your fucking bike, or you and your fucking bike in the fucking canal. The boy spluttered wordlessly. The handyman smiled, well, which is it? All right, all right! The boy wriggled to the ground. You're fucking crazy. I'll go.

It had gone quiet on the tables along the canal side. People looked from the handyman to the boy and back again. When the boy had walked round the side of the building, the handyman picked up his beer. He looked around and seeing that people were staring at him, he gestured at the saplings. They're fucking beautiful eh?
And everyone had to agree with him.

Pig's Ears

A man from Pig's Ears has been delivering beer to the car park for years now. Every week he delivers casks to the three other bars around the car park with no issues. Then he comes to us. The bar staff tell him to take the casks across the car park to the warehouse behind the brewery and the warehouse staff send the casks back to the bar and so on until either the bar or warehouse staff relent and say, fine we'll take them, as if they are doing him a favour. This happens because the casks belong in the warehouse but the warehouse staff get in trouble with the manager if the delivery note is not signed off by someone from the bar. No one who works in the bar or warehouse seems to remember the man from the week before, even though he has been coming to this car park for years, so the confusion always takes at least twenty minutes to resolve. The man never raises his voice or swears. He does not care in the slightest what happens to the beer. He is getting paid for his time and anyway, he has been thinking about leaving the company for years.

The Handyman

The handyman has a hard time of it because at any particular moment several parts of the bar are usually falling apart. The whole place is held together by cable ties, masking tape, cling film and expanding foam. The gas pipe behind the oven is always coming loose and has to be kicked in again and it is not unusual for staff to get mild electric shocks from the glass washer.

Once a week the handyman comes to the bar to fill the holes in the wall facing the canal. We know he resents being here and we offer him tea or coffee but he refuses. He hunkers down in the corner of the bar, pushes his grey hair out of his face and sets to work, all the while muttering about how he came to this city to be a fucking filmmaker—or at least a cameraman—and he sure as hell hadn't come halfway round the fucking world to spray stupid fucking expanding foam into fucking rat holes which they were going to eat through by the end of the fucking week anyway. We stand awkwardly behind him as he works, wanting to help him but knowing there is nothing we can do.

The Actors

In our bar there are three actors. Last year they applied for drama school and did not get in but they are applying again this year. They are in their mid-twenties, good-looking and do great impressions of people. Everyone is certain they will make it. When they are drunk they confide in us that what they really want is not to get into drama school but to get an agent. If they had an agent they could go for TV advertisements and earn a bit of money. They could stop working in the bar and really concentrate on their acting.

This summer a girl started working at the bar. She was eighteen and wore braces. She told everyone she wanted to be an actor. When she told the actors they smiled sadly. It takes a long time, one said. And another, you have to be really tough. She shrugged, I'll see how I do this summer.

At the end of August the girl announced she was quitting. An agent had picked her up and put her forward for a Channel 4 TV show. The audition had gone well and she was starting filming in a few weeks. That's amazing, we said, crowding round, hugging and kissing her, slapping her on the back. Then we realised the actors were not there. They were leaning on the bar a little apart from us, with fixed, stretched smiles. When the series came out no one watched or mentioned it.

The In-laws

It happened the other day that one of the girls brought her parents into the bar for lunch. They were visiting town for the day. Everyone made a point of saying hello. We gave the impression that their child was the most important, popular and beautiful person in the bar.

It is always exciting to host one of the parents. How we fuss! We clear people off tables to make room for them. Try all the beers for free, we say, try all the wines. The girls flirt with the fathers; the boys flirt with the mothers. We do everything we can to show them their child is in good hands. We are like the child's in-laws, though there is no spouse. Or perhaps we are the spouse? Your child is married to us now, we say with our bright smiles. She has found a new family. Look how much happier she is with us than she was with you.

Mia and Vincent

This spring two swans made a nest among the reed beds on the canal in front of the bar. From that day on they were always there. Sometimes the male would go away for a few hours but the female never left. It was only when she stood to rearrange her wings that we saw the eggs. They were larger than any we had seen, white with blue veins.

We named the swans Mia and Vincent and talked about them incessantly. Where did Vincent go every day? Was Mia eating enough? Did swans get prenatal depression? Were the eggs the right temperature? When would they hatch? Would they be boys or girls and how could we tell? It was all we could talk about.

One day when Vincent was away, Mia was attacked. Two swans came flying low over the canal towards the nest. Mia rose to defend it and they pecked at her breast and beat her with their wings. We shouted and waved our arms and one of us climbed onto the reed beds and scared them off with a broom.

We wanted to keep watch but it was weekday lunchtime and the bar was filling with customers, mostly mothers, buggies and babies. We are indifferent to all three. The mothers are demanding customers, complaining about the cleanliness of the toilets and asking for endless amendments to their food order. The buggies are annoying, taking up all the space in the bar and making it hard to run food to the tables. Then there are the babies. They are so alien. We look at them and wonder if we could ever make one. We do not have partners to make them with, or anywhere clean and quiet to put them or any money or time to spend on them. They are so wrinkly and ugly. We think perhaps we will never want one.

When the lunch rush was over, we went outside. Mia was gone. The two new swans strutted around the reed beds but did not seem at all interested in the eggs.

The sun set and still Mia and Vincent did not come back. We worried about the eggs. They would be cold. After we had closed the bar we went out with torches and a cardboard wine box lined with towels. We climbed onto the reed beds, lifted the eggs from the nest and laid them gently in the box. We put the box on the sofa and took it in turns to sit beside it and keep the eggs warm with the heat from our bodies. We spoke in whispers and played only the most ambient of electronic music—some tracks almost a lullaby—because we were afraid of waking the swan babies we imagined sleeping inside the great white eggs.

In the morning we called a specialist swan rescue charity and within an hour a brisk, stocky woman pulled up in the car park. When she saw the box she tutted. You should never move swan eggs, she said, they are probably dead now—even the slightest movement can separate the membrane from the egg. She must have seen how exhausted and emotionally invested we were because she added, well there's a chance they're alive. I'll take them back and put them in the incubator.

We thanked her and offered her a drink but she raised an eyebrow and said it was a little early for her. When she left we went out onto the back steps to wave her off. She glanced at us in the windscreen mirror and shook her head. We must have seemed an odd family. The following day she called to say the eggs were unfertilised.

Now the nest is covered with reeds and rubbish. The new swans are not interested in starting a family. In that respect they are better suited to the bar. All the same, we have not named them.

Half a Watermelon

The actor gave birth to half a watermelon this morning. We had been up all night at a forest party in the woods across the canal. At about eight in the morning the police came and told everyone to start winding up. We stumbled across the B road to the marshes and lay on the yellow grass. A few of us had taken acid. The actor started groaning and twitching. What's wrong? we said but he did not answer. He pulled half a watermelon from between his legs and glared at it in amazement and anger. Then he sank his face into the wet pink flesh and ate it.

Union

Neither of them had intended to have sex but they did and that was that. A month later, she discovered she was pregnant. Upon seeing the blue crosshair she decided to go out. At six in the morning, when she had been drinking and taking speed for almost twelve hours, she decided to call him. He was in another city and he too was out and drunk and high. I'm pregnant, she said. Fuck, he said, I'm sorry. Yeah, she said. She had gone out the fire escape door and was standing on the flat roof of the warehouse. She could see her breath in the air, the lights of the financial district in the distance. It was like the city in a movie. I'm gonna keep it, she said. Oh my god, he said, oh my god! This is gonna be so cool. And they both laughed hysterically.

The sun had set by the time she woke. She padded to the kitchen, filled a two litre bottle with water and went back to bed. The following day she called him to say that actually, no, she would not be keeping it.

Mount Everest

He smiled so much and so widely that at first we thought he was mad. He was from Denmark, via Berlin and the party never stopped for him. He was always smiling and he made us smile too. Even when it was so busy in the summer that the queue at the bar was all the way out the door, every table was dirty and there was broken glass under the canal side benches, even when we were out of lemonade, house red and house white, the IPA keg needed changing, food tickets spilled from the kitchen printer fixed to the wall down to the floor and the sous-chef was screaming Runner! Runner! Runner!, even when the legs of the floor staff ached after twenty kilometres, the arms of the bar staff ached after four hundred pints, the kitchen staff were drenched with sweat after rolling four hundred bases and there was a gaggle of people at the no-service area shouting abuse because they had waited forty minutes, an hour, over two hours for their pizza and we were each moving fast and silent, our jaws clenched and our faces blank as we tried to keep the whole show on the road for just one more minute, even then he would be smiling, his light blue eyes wide as saucers—and if he passed one of us on the floor he would grip our arm and say, can you imagine, man, that in a universe a fraction of a centimetre away from this one, we are standing at the top of Mount Everest!

The Promotion

One day the bar manager turned up to work wearing a red bandana. This was before he became the manager. He had been up all night taking a mixture of amphetamines and hallucinogens. He could not speak clearly and his hand-eye co-ordination was limited. He must have lost his inhibition too because we saw him pulling down one side of his shirt and encouraging a customer to touch his nipple. The bar staff told him to go home but he insisted he was okay and wanted to work. At some point he went to the toilet and fell asleep for four hours. When he came back the bar staff tried again to send him home. He refused to believe he had been asleep for four hours and worked on until the end of his shift. He has a great work ethic in his way. It was shortly after this that he was promoted to manager.

The Last One That Summer

There was something wrong with the last person they hired that summer. It was as if the manager had lost the enthusiasm to interview people thoroughly. He had never worked in a bar and did not want to learn. He spoke quickly and continuously and often interrupted us to make anxious jibes. For example, if we said a table booking was bigger than expected, he would say—said the actress to the bishop!—and nudge us until we acknowledged him. Everything had to be footnoted with a joke. It was exhausting. We smiled politely when he spoke but did not reply or meet his eye in case he carried on talking. It did not always work. He could talk about a topic more or less on his own for over an hour. If he was behind the bar, we found excuses to leave: to run food, clean tables, take out the bins, anything but be near him. After a few weeks of this, he emailed to say he had found another job. He must have got the hint, we thought. But a month or so later he came into the bar to drink. We greeted him hesitantly but he was unabashed, apparently either bearing no grudges or not being the slightest bit aware we had not liked him.

The Oddball

A certain man comes to the bar every Saturday afternoon. He never buys anything but pours himself a glass of water and sits on one of the canal side tables staring at the water. He wears fingerless gloves, a thick beanie hat and orange-tinted ski goggles in all weathers. The owners have repeatedly asked us to throw him out but we never do. It pleases us to think of ourselves as so accepting of difference.

The Awkward Boy

There was once an awkward boy who loved bikes. In spite of his awkwardness, he was easy to talk to because we always knew what to ask him about. He loved bikes so much he never suspected we were humouring him. His bike was always blocking the fire exit or toilets because it was too precious to leave outside. He posted videos online of him riding bikes, or photos of his new bikes or of bike gear he had bought. When there was a lock-in he danced on his fixie in front of the DJ booth, standing on the pedals and moving back and forth. If the beat intensified he might do a little jump to the side and back and if it was downtempo he might pedal silently around the bar. We smirked at each other when he did this and some cruel part of us always hoped he would fall off but he never did.

One time he told us he would be coming to the bar with his cycling club. Fifty of us, he said. We were sure he did not know so many people, but when the day came they clattered into the bar, laughing loudly and making jokes about bikes we did not understand. To our surprise we could see he was a big deal in the cycling club but we said nothing. They bought their drinks and returned to the car park to be with their bikes. One of them had a wireless speaker clipped to his handlebar and all night long they played music and danced on their bikes, like mermaids rolling in the wash of the street lights.

Like Us

Once the customers were like us. Many worked in bars and were trying to make it as artists on the side. When we were not working we would drink with them. Now they are not like us. They do not work in bars and are not trying to make it as artists on the side. They click their fingers to be served and do not care how expensive the Prosecco is.

The King of the Rats

The problem started when one of the customers saw a rat running along the side of the bar. She sent an email complaining about the rat and demanding a refund on her food. She was happy to come in to collect the refund in cash, she wrote, because she lived nearby.

The email remained unread until Thursday because the manager was suffering from a hangover for three consecutive days. The bar email account was eventually checked by the owners who called an emergency meeting. Present at the meeting were: the owners, the manager and the operations officer.

The operations officer was hired because he was so good at getting things done. When you asked him what he did that is what he said. He said, I get things done. He made sure we saved his number on our phone so we could call him if we ever wanted anything done.

By the end of the meeting everyone agreed the rats had to be killed. It was not the rats themselves that were the problem but the fact the rats had been seen. There had always been rats. The bar had been built in a slapdash manner because no one had expected it to be a success. There were holes in the walls and large un-insulated gaps above the ceiling.

The bar staff had always known about the rats. When the last customer had left, everything was cleaned and the shutters were down, they sat on the sofas, drank, smoked, took tranquilisers and played ambient techno to help them unwind. They heard the rats running around in the gap between the ceiling and the upstairs floor.

But now one of the customers had seen a rat, something had to be done. When the meeting was over, the operations officer drove to the local cash and carry and haggled until he got a good price for sixty extra strength foldable glue board traps. That evening when the last customer had left the manager instructed the staff to distribute the glue traps around the bar. Some of the bar staff were vegans and proudly refused to have anything to do with the traps and those who were not refused in solidarity. So it fell to the manager to lay the traps every evening.

Every morning for the next few weeks he would find rats stuck to the glue. They were still alive and twitching. He folded the traps in half and pressed on them with his foot to put the rats out of their misery. Then he put the traps into a bin bag and threw it away. Slowly, the rats entered the manager's dreams and the dreams of the bar staff too. For however much the manager tried to take it on himself, they knew the bin bags were full of blood and fur matted with glue. It was worst for the kitchen staff because when they rolled the pizza bases they saw the flattened bodies of the rats.

One morning the manager came in to find three glue traps piled on top of each other. When he went closer he saw a rat larger than any he had seen before. It had run across one glue trap but, because of its enormous force and velocity, the glue trap had not stopped it. Instead, it had carried the trap on its haunches until it reached the second glue trap. But this too had not stopped it. It had dragged this on until it reached the third glue trap and there it had been stopped.

In time the rats no longer came to the bar. By then most of the staff who believed in the right of an animal to a dignified death had gone and for the most part the new staff did not believe in that sort of thing. The manager had been replaced too. Only the operations officer remained and to him the rats were just another thing that he had done.

The New Manager

No one likes the new manager. He wears Ralph Lauren polo shirts and cracks his knuckles when he speaks. The first time he met us he talked a lot about how he had quit his old job because it was getting too corporate and straight and how much he loved the raw energy of the bar. I love the raw energy of the bar, he said, shaking his hand in front of him, palm upward and fingers curled, as if squeezing life out of a rodent.

Clarke, Nickolls & Coombs

Every hour on the hour on weekend afternoons, there are tours of the brewery. Before she takes them across the car park to the brewery, the guide tells the customers that this used to be an industrial area. There were factories producing all sorts: crepe silk, synthetic ivory, chocolate, toilet paper, as well as the country's first ever dry cleaning company. The warehouses around this car park were built in 1897 by the confectionary company Clarke, Nickolls & Coombs, who employed all the women living in the grid of terraced houses on the south side of the island. The company had its own ambulance and fire engine, a brass band that toured abroad and a 100 person choral society. When a woman married, Mister Clarke always made sure the company provided her with a dowry. To check the customers are still listening, the guide says that everyone at Clarke, Nickolls & Coombs had names like Lippy Lil and Big Billy and sang as they worked.

We hear this spiel every hour on the hour on weekend afternoons. We are not interested in the slightest. We do not care that the warehouses round here were closed when Clarnico was sold to Trebor Sharps or that Trebor Sharps was taken over by Cadbury which in turn was bought out by Kraft. We do not care about history. Anyway, the brewery will be shut down soon because the owners are opening a new, larger one farther out of town. Elsewhere craft ale start-ups are being bought out by big multi-national beverage companies. It does not affect us. We live in the grid of terraced houses on the south side of the island. We have names like Little Luke and Ian Party Harder and we sing while we work.

Close and Open

Opening the bar is just closing it in reverse. When we close we take in the napkins, salt and pepper shakers and chilli oil, we wipe the tables and stack the benches on top. When we open we take back down the benches, wipe the tables and put out the napkins, salt and pepper shakers and chilli oil. The shutters that went down must go up again, the awnings that were in go out, the heaters that were off go on. The glass washer must be drained, turned off and disassembled at night and in the morning it is reassembled, turned on and filled up. Everything that is undone is done again. Sometimes you are on the rota to close the bar one day and open it the next. It is natural at this time to reflect upon the pointlessness of it all.